We're Roaming in the Rainforest

An Amazon Adventure

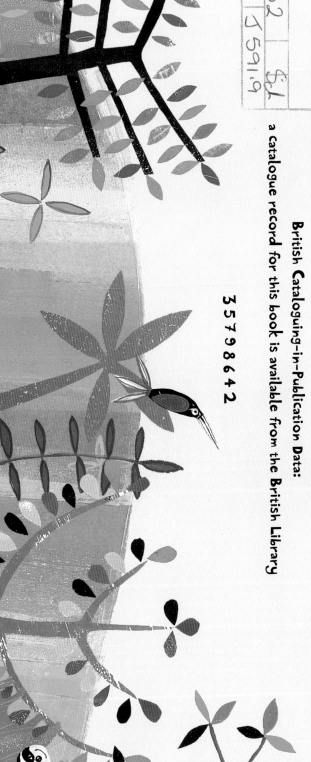

For Connie, Lynn and Nancy: all dear friends — L. K.

Many thanks to Dr. Paul Beaver of Amazonia Expeditions for sharing
with the author his knowledge of the peoples of the rainforest.

For Simone, always in our hearts x — A. W.

Barefoot Books • 124 Walcot Street • Bath, BA1 5BG

Text copyright © 2010 by Laurie Krebs. Illustrations copyright © 2010 by Anne Wilson.
The moral rights of Laurie Krebs and Anne Wilson have been asserted.
First published in Great Britain in 2010 by Barefoot Books, Ltd.

Graphic design by Louise Millar, London. Reproduction by B&P International, Hong Kong.

This book was typeset in Potato Cut.
The illustrations were prepared with printed papers, printing ink and acrylic paints.

ISBN 978-1-84686-330-1

British Cataloguing-in-Publication Data:
a catalogue record for this book is available from the British Library

3 5 7 9 8 6 4 2

We're Roaming in the Rainforest

An Amazon Adventure

Written by Laurie Krebs

Illustrated by Anne Wilson

Barefoot Books
Celebrating Art and Story

Rainforest sunrise. The dark fades away.
And everyone eagerly greets the new day.

"Fly," squawk the parrots,
from branches and twigs.
"We'll swoop down to breakfast
on ripe, juicy figs."

"Jump," chatter monkeys.
"Or swing if you dare."

"We'll hang by our tails and then leap through the air."

"Snooze," yawn the sloths, all ready to doze.

"Sip," murmur butterflies,
high in the sky.
"We'll lunch upon nectar
as we flutter by."

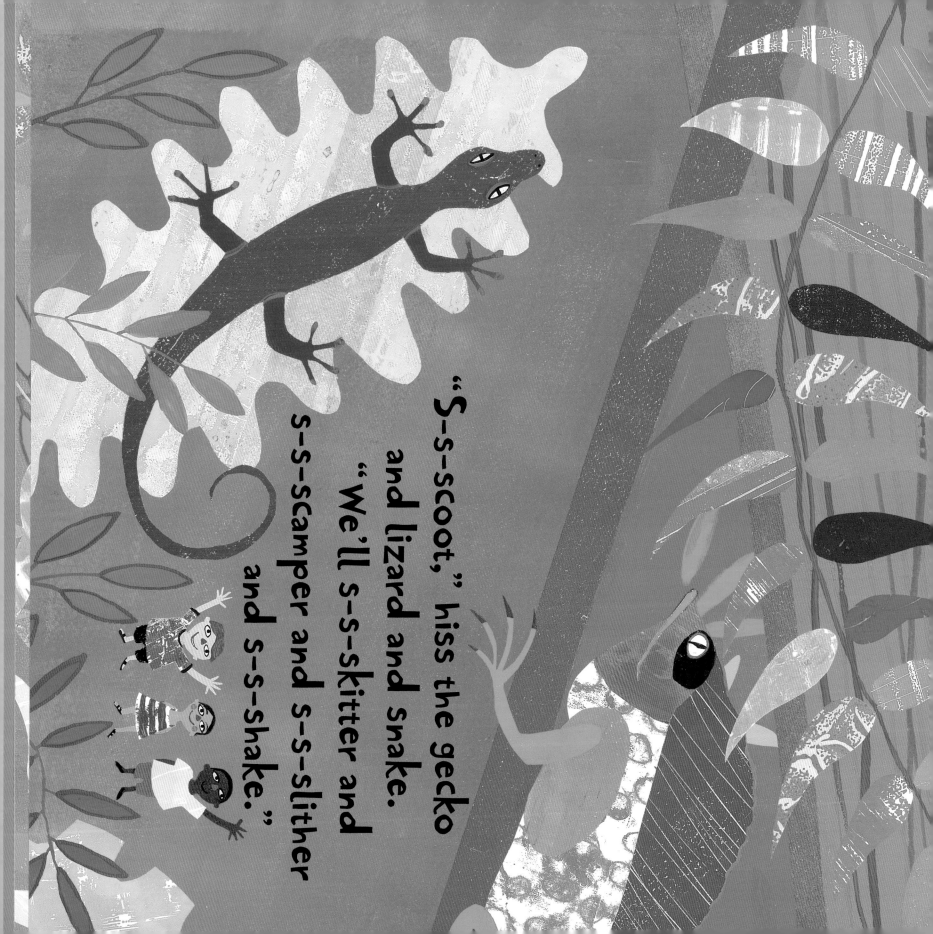

"S-s-scoot," hiss the gecko
and lizard and snake.
"We'll s-s-skitter and
s-s-scamper and s-s-slither
and s-s-shake."

"Crouch," growl the jaguars
as dusk closes in.
"We'll hide until dark,
when our hunt can begin."

"Hush," whisper otters
to pups in a heap.
"We'll cuddle together
till we fall asleep."

Rainforest sunset.
The moon's on the rise.
And everyone listens
to night's lullabies.

The Amazon Rainforest

There is no place in the world quite like the Amazon rainforest of South America. Most of the Amazon rainforest is in Brazil, but it also spreads into Venezuela, Colombia, Ecuador, Peru and Bolivia. It is the largest tropical rainforest on earth and home to many, many plants, animals and people. A very important part of our ecosystem, the rainforest contains trees and plants that help us breathe by changing carbon dioxide into oxygen. For this reason, the rainforest is often called the "lungs of our planet".

The Amazon River is the most extensive river system in the world. Beginning as a trickle in the Andes Mountains of Peru, it travels more than four thousand miles across Brazil to the Atlantic Ocean. Its rivers, streams and tributaries — the branches of a river — flow through Colombia, Venezuela, Ecuador, Bolivia and the three Guyanas. The Amazon River provides two-thirds of the earth's fresh water and beneath its surface live more than two thousand kinds of fish.

Nearly half a million species of plants have been recorded in the Amazon rainforest. One-fifth of the world's birds, hundreds of mammals, more than a thousand varieties of frogs and an amazing number of reptiles and insects are found there. Scientists believe even more plants and animals are yet to be discovered. People have lived in the rainforest for thousands of years, sometimes along the river, sometimes deep in the jungle. When plants, animals and people live in balance with one another, the rainforest thrives.

SOUTH AMERICA

ATLANTIC OCEAN

Caribbean Sea

VENEZUELA

GUYANA

SURINAME

FRENCH GUIANA

COLOMBIA

ECUADOR

The Amazon River

THE AMAZON RAINFOREST

BRAZIL

PERU

BOLIVIA

PARAGUAY

CHILE

ARGENTINA

URUGUAY

PACIFIC OCEAN

Conservation

Today, the human population of the rainforest has grown by leaps and bounds as business people around the world discover the Amazon's riches. Corporations are sending workers to log its trees, mine its gold and set up cattle ranches. Roads serving these industries are carved through the forest, destroying wildlife. Thousands of acres are burned to clear land for farms. Sadly, the rainforest is shrinking and many native plants and animals have disappeared forever. As people move into the area to serve the companies, local tribes, who once counted in their millions, are shrinking in number.

Scientists and conservationists are working to protect and preserve the rainforest. They are sharing new ideas to bring money to the area and provide support for the people living there. Native trees and plants are often destroyed by slash-and-burn farming, but we need to allow them to stand in order to provide an ongoing supply of nutritious nuts, oils and healing medicines. New trees are being planted and improved farming methods are being developed. Local people are trained for the tourist industry, which helps to pay for medical care and village schools. Governments are encouraged to pass laws protecting the rainforest. These efforts are helping to restore the delicate balance of this important, enchanting place.

Please contact the following organisations to find out how you can help:

Oxfam: www.oxfam.org

Survival International: www.survivalinternational.org

The Woodland Trust: www.woodlandtrust.org.uk

The Prince's Rainforests Project: www.rainforestsos.org

The Creatures of the Amazon Rainforest

The Amazon rainforest is home to many creatures, large and small.

Here are the ones pictured in this book:

Short-Tailed Parrots — Beautiful, intelligent and playful, Amazonian parrots were among the first creatures Christopher Columbus saw in the New World. They are especially noisy in the early morning and at dusk.

Spider Monkeys — Spider monkeys live in social groups called troops. They are great acrobats and can leap from a tree branch on one side of a narrow river to a branch on the other side.

Three-Toed Sloths — Sloths are slow-moving, shy mammals that spend most of their lives hanging upside down from tree branches. They sleep many hours of the day but are more active at night.

Pink River Dolphins — With flexible bodies and friendly, curious natures, pink river dolphins have been known to push drowning villagers safely ashore when their canoes have overturned.

Blue Morpho Butterflies — Tiny scales on their wings reflect light and produce the brilliant colour of the blue morpho butterflies. Ancient people thought butterflies were angels because their folded wings looked like praying hands.

Black Caimans — Meat-eating reptiles, black caimans live in freshwater areas of the rainforest. They are excellent swimmers, with webbed feet and powerful tails that propel them through the water.

Poison Dart Frogs — These colourful frogs, smaller than a thumbnail, have poisonous skin. Predators, tasting the poison, get very sick and quickly learn to leave the frogs alone.

Leaf-Cutter Ants — Leaf-cutter ants are the world's first farmers. They carry pieces of leaves to their nests and chew them into pulp. A special fungus, growing on the pulp, is their food.

Spiders — Web-weaving spiders spin sticky threads to capture insects and then paralyse them with their venom. Hunting spiders, like tarantulas, use poisonous fangs or powerful jaws to kill their prey.

Green Iguanas — One of many rainforest lizards, green iguanas grow to be six feet long. Young lizards hunt for insects and worms on the forest floor. Adults live in trees and feast mostly on plants.

Geckos

Geckos — Geckos are the only lizards that have voices. Their clicking, squeaking noise sounds just like their name, "gecko". They have sticky toe pads to help them climb smooth surfaces.

Anacondas

Anacondas — Anacondas, members of the boa family, are among the largest, most powerful snakes in the world. Although most baby snakes hatch from eggs, mother anacondas, like humans, give birth to living young.

Jaguars

Jaguars — Jaguars are large, solitary cats that are now quite rare in the wild. Among ancient people, they were identified with royalty as symbols of power, strength and bravery in warfare.

Giant River Otters

Giant River Otters — River otter families live in mud caves along the banks of lakes and rivers. Stubby feet make the otters awkward on land but strong, flattened tails help them to be swift and agile swimmers.

At Barefoot Books, we celebrate art and story that opens the hearts and minds of children from all walks of life, inspiring them to read deeper, search further, and explore their own creative gifts. Taking our inspiration from many different cultures, we focus on themes that encourage independence of spirit, enthusiasm for learning, and sharing of the world's diversity. Interactive, playful and beautiful, our products combine the best of the present with the best of the past to educate our children as the caretakers of tomorrow.

Barefoot Books
Celebrating Art and Story

Live Barefoot!
Join us at www.barefootbooks.com